'Ouch! That Hurts!'

by
David Orme

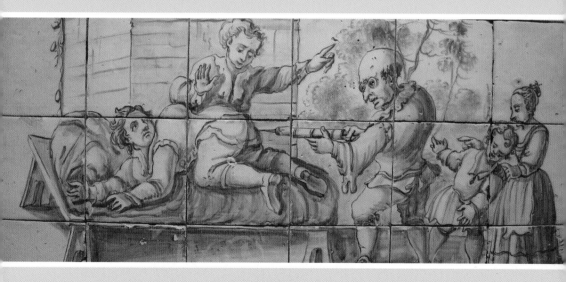

Thunderbolts

'Ouch! That Hurts!'
by David Orme

Illustrated by Demitri The Krah

Published by Ransom Publishing Ltd.
Radley House, 8 St. Cross Road, Winchester, Hants. SO23 9HX, UK
www.ransom.co.uk

ISBN   978 178127 078 3

First published in 2013

Illustrations copyright © 2013 Demitri The Krah
'Get the Facts' section - images copyright: cover, prelims, passim – Stigur Karlsson, Jenny O'Donnell,
Yelkrokoyade; pp 6/7 - Nick Webley, Wolfgang Sauber, Rama, Michal Maňas, Luigi Chiesa; pp 8/9 - Niko Guido,
MrArifnajafov, Luc Viatour; pp 10/11 - Daniel Mirer Photographer, kim traynor; pp 14/15 - Wouter van Caspel,
Steven Wynn; pp 16/17 - Jenny O'Donnell; pp 18/19 - Factoria Singular, Stigur Karlsson; pp 20/21 - Miguel Malo;
pp 22/23 - Jim Thurston, Jon Bodsworth; p 36 - Jenny O'Donnell.

A CIP catalogue record of this book is available from the British Library.

Contents

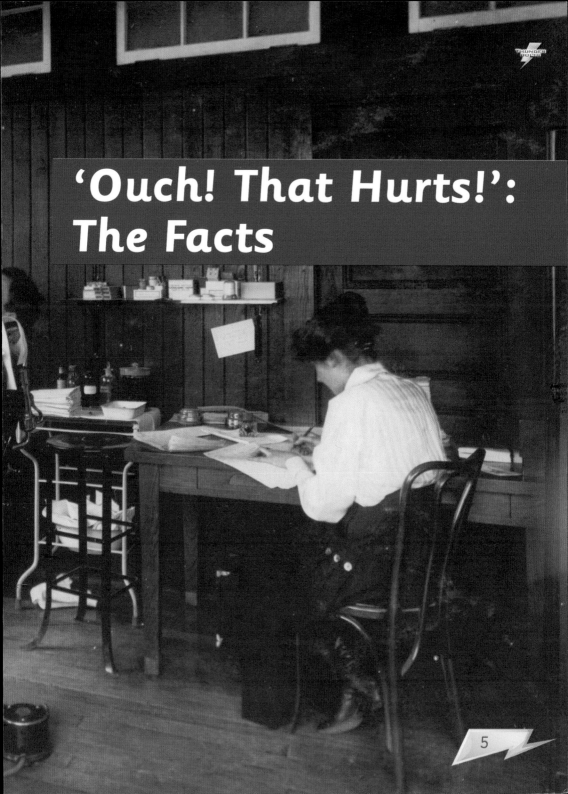

'Ouch! That Hurts!': The Facts

Stone-age surgery

When did surgery start?

Surgery started in the stone age.

What did they do?

They cut holes in your head.

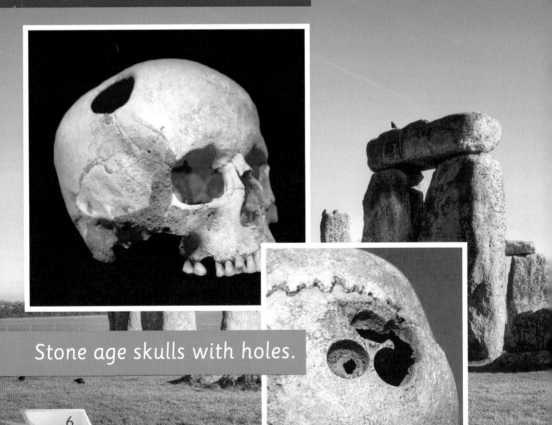

Stone age skulls with holes.

They could cut off injured arms.

What did they use? Sharp pieces of flint.

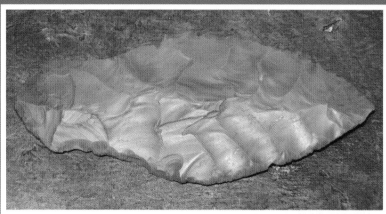

Did it hurt?

Yes! But there are plants that can make it less painful.

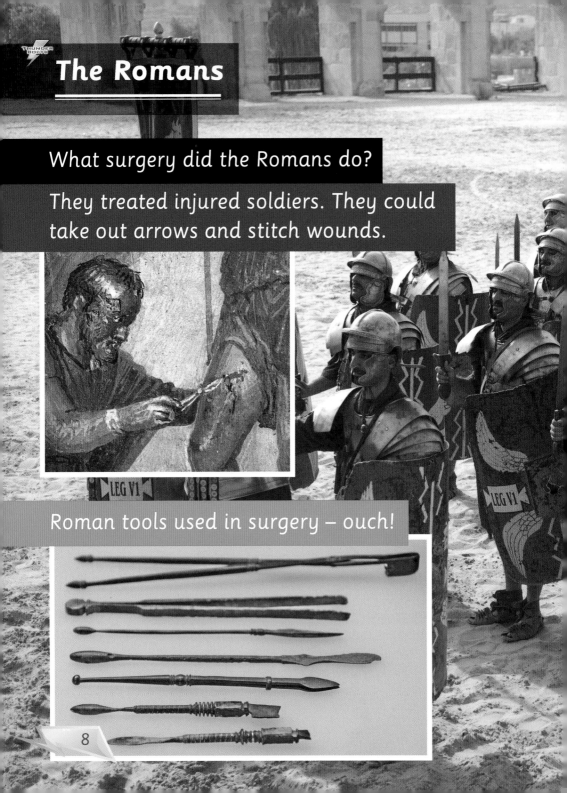

The Romans

What surgery did the Romans do?

They treated injured soldiers. They could take out arrows and stitch wounds.

Roman tools used in surgery – ouch!

8

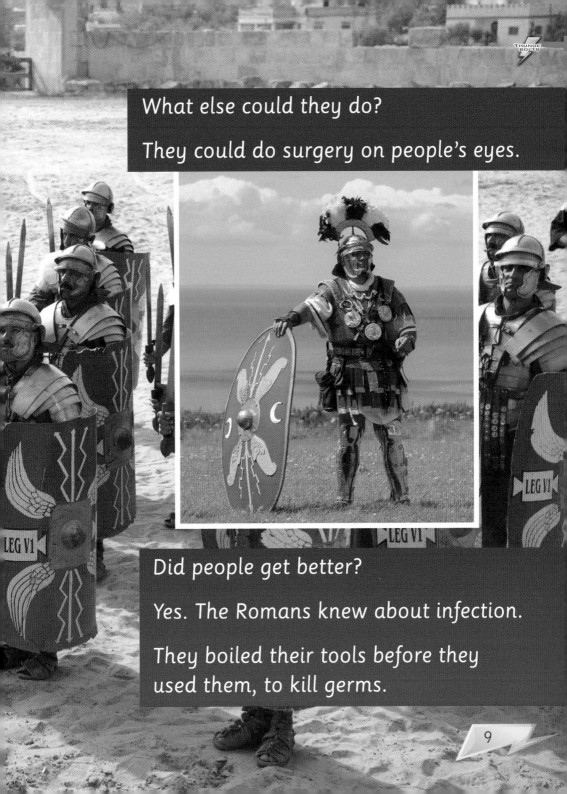

What else could they do?

They could do surgery on people's eyes.

Did people get better?

Yes. The Romans knew about infection.

They boiled their tools before they used them, to kill germs.

Haircut and a leg off, sir?

If you had a toothache in medieval times, where would you go?

Answer: to the hairdressers!

Barber surgeons could:

- Treat wounds
- Pull out rotten teeth
- Take blood from you

– and even cut off arms and legs.

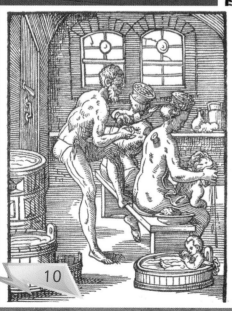

Why would they want to take your blood?

They thought that getting rid of some blood would cure all sorts of things.

Did it? No.

Barber surgeons used this sign. Hairdressers still use it today.

What do you think it means?

Surgery on board ship

This is Lord Nelson.

He lost his right arm in a sea battle in 1797.

Each ship had a surgeon. They treated the men for wounds and any illness.

Fighting at sea caused many wounds. Surgeons often had to cut off arms and legs.

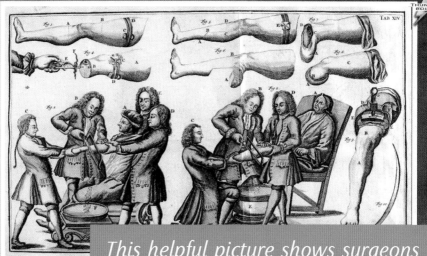

This helpful picture shows surgeons where to cut!

Did it hurt?

Yes! The sailors had a bullet put in their mouth to bite on.

Did that help?

No. But it stopped them screaming!

What happened to Nelson's arm?

They threw it in the sea!

Body snatchers

Surgeons needed to practise.

People didn't want to be practised on!

What did they use? Dead bodies.

That was a problem.

They couldn't use the bodies of people who died in hospital.

They used these bodies:

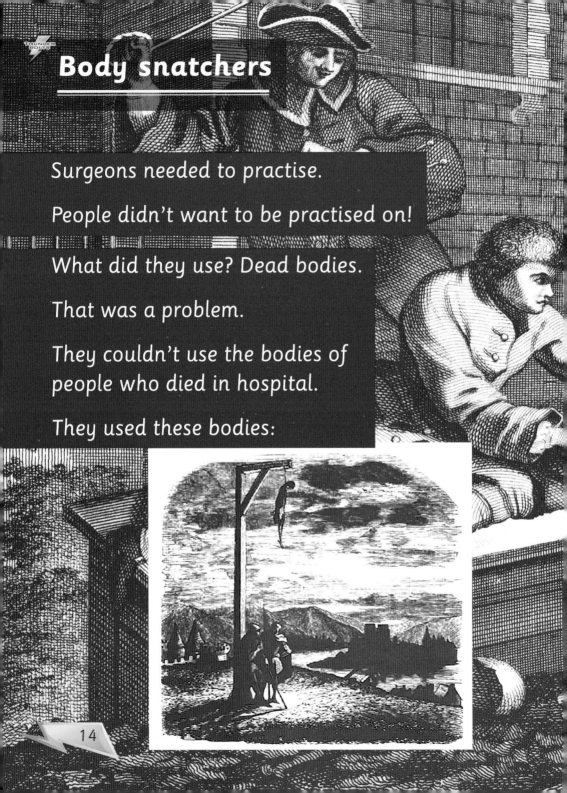

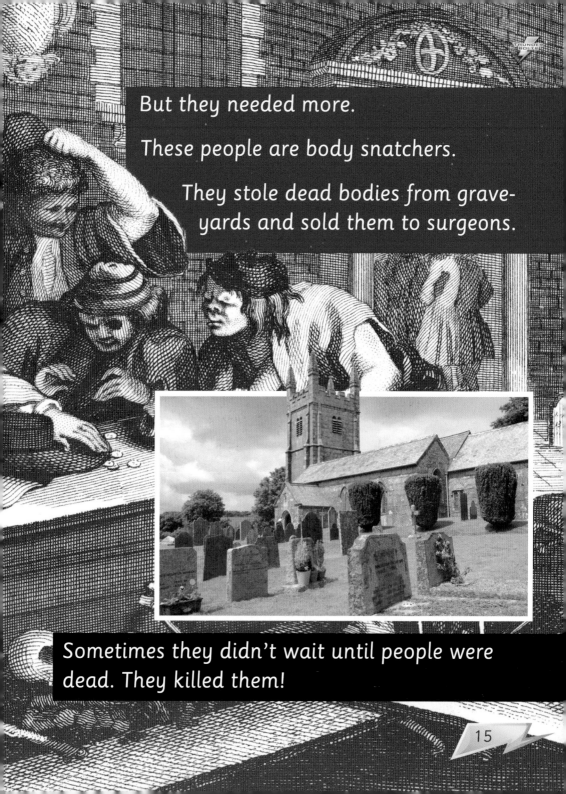

But they needed more.

These people are body snatchers.

They stole dead bodies from grave-yards and sold them to surgeons.

Sometimes they didn't wait until people were dead. They killed them!

This is a Victorian operating theatre.

The operating table is in the middle. All around are places for people to watch the operation.

Why?

They were learning how to be surgeons.

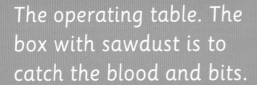

The operating table. The box with sawdust is to catch the blood and bits.

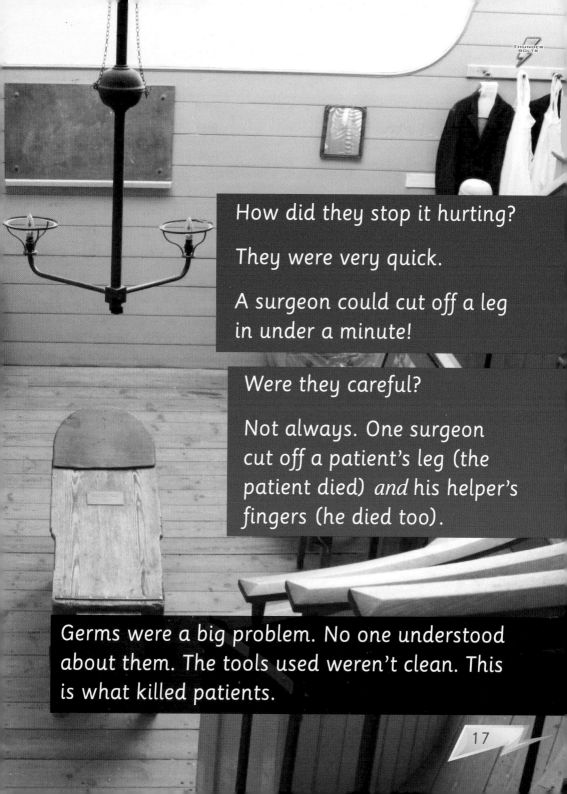

How did they stop it hurting?

They were very quick.

A surgeon could cut off a leg in under a minute!

Were they careful?

Not always. One surgeon cut off a patient's leg (the patient died) *and* his helper's fingers (he died too).

Germs were a big problem. No one understood about them. The tools used weren't clean. This is what killed patients.

Stopping it hurting

In the nineteenth century surgeons found gasses that would put people to sleep.

Then they could operate on the patients while they were asleep.

The first operation using an *anaesthetic* – 1846.

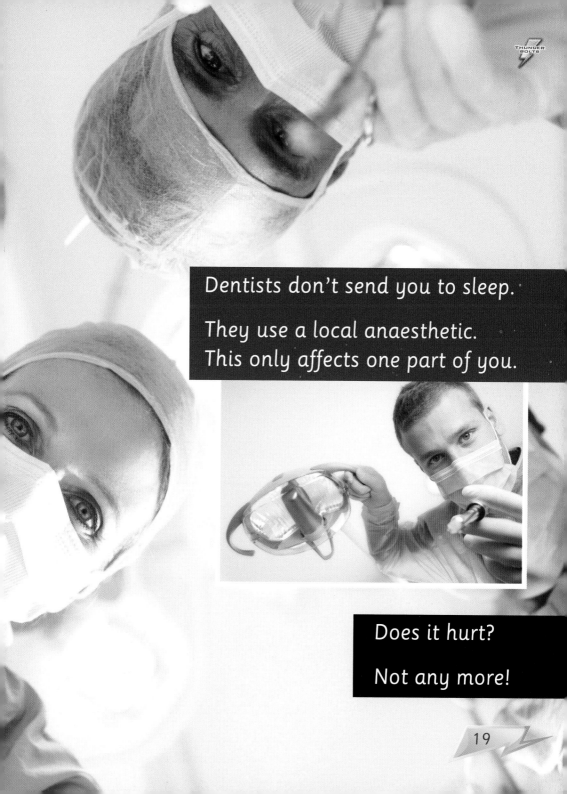

Dentists don't send you to sleep.

They use a local anaesthetic.
This only affects one part of you.

Does it hurt?

Not any more!

Operating theatres today

Surgeon

Mask

Operating table

Instruments

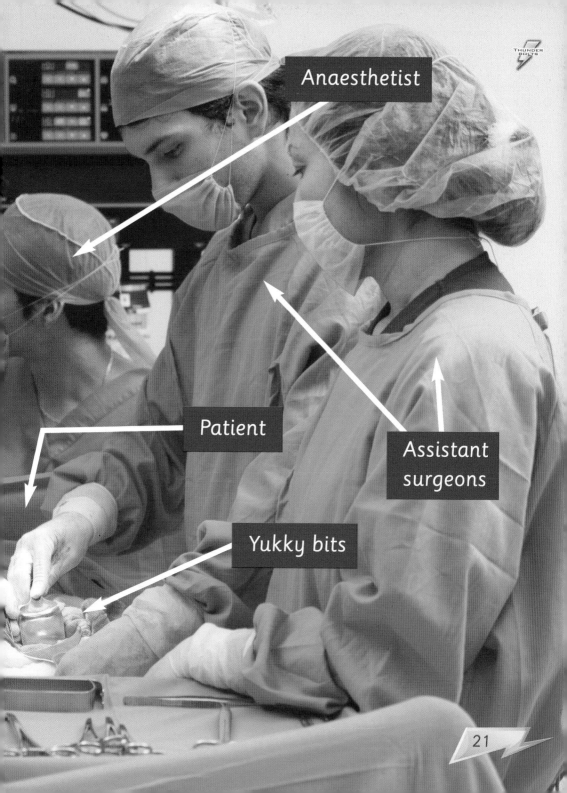

Anaesthetist

Assistant surgeons

Patient

Yukky bits

Amazing things surgeons can do

They can:

- Give you body parts like hearts, livers and kidneys from people who have died

- Replace worn-out joints like hips or knees

- Treat really serious diseases like cancer.

If you lose an arm or a leg, surgeons can give you a new one!

Is this a new idea?

No! This is a foot from Egypt. It is over 3,000 years old.

The person has been given a new toe made out of wood!

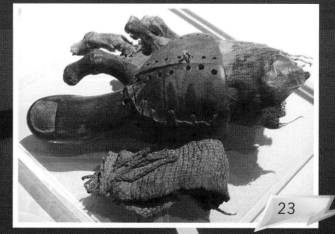

The Choice

Jed is hiking through the Rocky Mountains.

The weather has turned bad. He is sheltering under some rocks.

This is a bad idea, Jed!

The rain got worse. Jed thought he would get some sleep.

But something was happening at the top of the cliff.

Jed, you had better wake up – **NOW!**

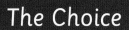
Too late!

A huge rock has fallen on to Jed's arm. He's trapped!

He has a mobile phone in his bag, but he can't reach it!

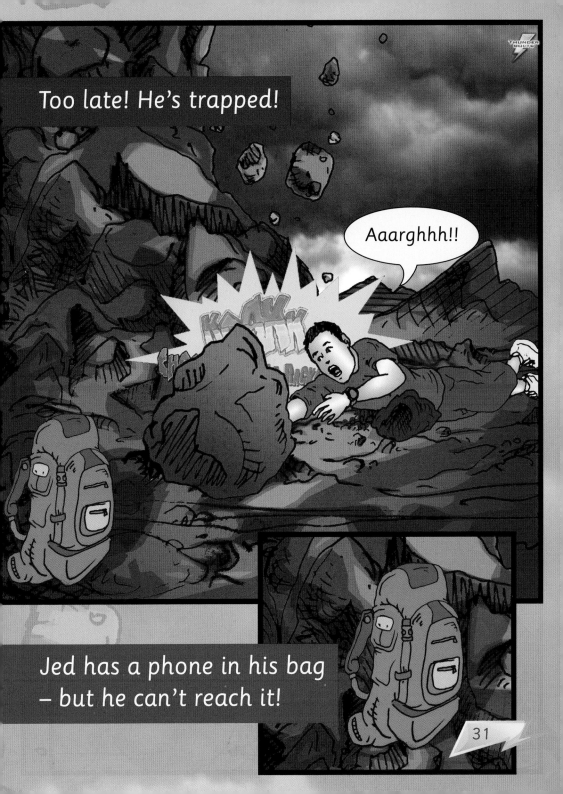

It's night time.

How long can Jed last without food and water?

And there's another problem – bears!

It's night time. Jed needs food and water.

This bear is hungry! How can Jed save himself?

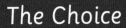

There's only one thing that Jed can do. But is he brave enough to do it?

Would **you** be brave enough?

(This is based on a true story that happened in 2003. Only names and places have been changed.)

Jed knows what he has to do
– but is he brave enough?

Yes!

Would **you** be brave enough?

Word list

anaesthetic
anaesthetist
body snatcher
cancer
dentist
disease
graveyard
infection
joint

medieval
mobile phone
operating theatre
operation
patient
surgeon
surgery
toothache
Victorian